# GOPAL MEASURES THE EARTH

GOPAL, THE CLEVER BARBER, HAD FREE ACCESS TO KRISHNA CHANDRA, THE KING OF KRISHNANAGAR IN BENGAL. BUT ONE DAY—

THE KING DOES NOT WISH TO SEE YOU.

THEN I **MUST** SEE HIM.

I'M HERE, YOUR MAJESTY. YOUR MAJESTY?

DON'T BOTHER ME NOW, GOPAL. I'M WORRIED.

KINGS DON'T WORRY, YOUR MAJESTY! THEY PAY PEOPLE TO DO IT FOR THEM.

OOOH! OWWW! MOTHER KALI, DIDN'T YOU KNOW I WAS ONLY JOKING? DON'T YOU HAVE A SENSE OF HUMOUR?

OF COURSE, YOU SHALL HAVE YOUR BUFFALO— FIVE BUFFALOES, ANYTHING YOU WANT— BUT PLEASE RID ME OF THIS PAIN!

HEE! HEE! NOW WASN'T THAT CLEVER OF MOTHER KALI?

NOT EVEN A SMILE! HE REALLY IS WORRIED.

YOUR MAJESTY! YOUR MAJESTY!!!

UH? WHAT?

OH, IT'S YOU. I THOUGHT I HAD TOLD YOU NOT TO BOTHER ME.

WHY DON'T YOU CONFIDE IN ME? PERHAPS I COULD HELP YOU, YOUR MAJESTY.

OH, ALL RIGHT! I WILL.

THE NAWAB OF MURSHIDABAD HAS ORDERED ME TO GET SOMEONE TO MEASURE THE LENGTH AND BREADTH OF THE EARTH.

IS THAT ALL?

ALL? ALL! WHAT DO YOU MEAN IS THAT ALL? WHERE AM I TO FIND SOMEONE WHO WILL TAKE ON SUCH AN IMPOSSIBLE TASK?

RIGHT HERE, YOUR MAJESTY. I'LL DO IT FOR YOU.

DON'T TRY MY PATIENCE, GOPAL!

THIS IS NOT A MATTER TO JOKE ABOUT. PERHAPS MY VERY LIFE IS AT STAKE.

I KNOW, YOUR MAJESTY. THAT'S WHY I SAY, LEAVE IT TO ME.

DO YOU KNOW WHAT WILL HAPPEN IF YOU FAIL? I WILL BE EXECUTED AND YOU WILL BE OUT OF A JOB!

NEITHER OF WHICH WILL HAPPEN, YOUR MAJESTY.

TRUST ME. ALL I'LL NEED IS TWENTY-FIVE BULLOCK CARTS.

BULLOCK CARTS?

YES. AND ALL THE SILK AND COTTON THREAD IN TOWN.

SO, A FEW DAYS LATER GOPAL LEFT FOR MURSHIDABAD AT THE HEAD OF A ROW OF BULLOCK CARTS.

WHEN HE REACHED THE NAWAB'S PALACE AT MURSHIDABAD —

YOU WAIT HERE. I'LL GO AND MEET THE NAWAB.

FROM KRISHNA CHANDRA DID YOU SAY?

YES, YOUR EXCELLENCY.

WHERE ARE THE MEASUREMENTS?

IF YOU STEP OUTSIDE FOR A MOMENT, I'LL GIVE THEM TO YOU, YOUR EXCELLENCY.

GOPAL TOOK THE NAWAB TO THE CARTS.

THE THREAD IN THE FIRST FOURTEEN CARTS PUT TOGETHER...

...IS THE LENGTH OF THE EARTH — AND THE REMAINING ELEVEN CART-LOADS, THE BREADTH.

BUT... BUT... WHAT IF IT ISN'T ACCURATE?

YOU COULD HAVE IT CHECKED. OR BETTER STILL, YOUR EXCELLENCY COULD PERSONALLY CHECK IT,

# GOPAL IN THE SWEET-SHOP

THE CHILDREN OF THE TOWN LOVED GOPAL FOR HE OFTEN JOINED THEM IN THEIR PRANKS. ONE SUMMER AFTERNOON—

WILL YOU DO SOMETHING FOR US?

I'M SURE HE WILL!

WILL YOU GET US SOME FREE SWEETS FROM BHOLA'S SWEET SHOP?

FREE SWEETS FROM THAT MAN? IMPOSSIBLE!

THE MAN CHEATS US EVEN WHEN WE PAY FOR THE SWEETS.

IS THAT SO? WELL, LEAVE HIM TO ME THEN AND GET READY FOR A FEAST!

IT'S ALMOST TIME FOR BHOLA'S AFTERNOON NAP.

TRUE ENOUGH, IT WAS.

I AM GOING IN FOR A NAP. WAKE ME UP IF ANYONE COMES AND DON'T LET ME CATCH YOU EATING THE SWEETS!

YES, FATHER.

WH.. WHO ARE YOU? WHAT ARE YOU DOING? STOP IT!

DON'T WORRY. YOUR FATHER KNOWS ME. YOU CAN TELL HIM I'M HERE!

BUT WHO ARE YOU?

JUST CALL ME MAKKHI.

# WHO IS THE MASTER ?

ONE DAY, GOPAL WAS ABOUT TO ENTER A SHOP WHEN THE SHOPKEEPER CAME UP BEHIND HIM.

HEY, GOPAL! KEEP YOUR DOG OUT OF MY SHOP!

MY DOG?

BUT THIS DOG ISN'T MINE.

NOT YOURS? OF COURSE IT IS! YOU ARE ITS MASTER.

IT WAS FOLLOWING YOU, WASN'T IT?

I SEE, THEN MY DOG MUST BE YOUR MASTER SINCE YOU WERE FOLLOWING IT!

AND IF YOU WANT TO KEEP YOUR MASTER OUT, DO IT YOURSELF.

# GOPAL AND THE THIEF

ONE NIGHT A THIEF BROKE INTO GOPAL'S HOUSE.

HAND OVER ALL YOUR GOLD ORNAMENTS! AND BE QUICK!

T...TAKE WHATEVER YOU WANT. B...BUT SPARE OUR LIVES.

JUST THEN THEY HEARD A SOUND.

WHAT'S THAT?

IT MUST BE ANOTHER THIEF TRYING TO BREAK IN.

WHO IS IT?

HUSH! QUIET!

WHAT'S THE MATTER? YOU LOOK WORRIED.

I'M DONE FOR! IT'S A GANG OF DACOITS.

THEY'LL BE HERE ANY MOMENT. THEY'LL MURDER ME. PLEASE PROTECT ME.

WHAT ABOUT US?

CALM DOWN, DEAR. GOD IS PROTECTING US.

ALL RIGHT! DON'T PANIC. WE'LL HIDE YOU TILL THEY'VE GONE.

OH, THANK YOU, SIR, THANK YOU.

NOW STAY THERE AND DON'T EVEN BREATHE. WE'LL GET RID OF THEM.

QUICK, COME WITH ME!

I'M OFF TO GET HELP. NOW LISTEN CAREFULLY AND DO EXACTLY AS I TELL YOU...

GOPAL LEFT BY THE FRONT DOOR.

PLEASE COME BACK SOON.

I WILL. DON'T FORGET TO DO EXACTLY AS I'VE TOLD YOU.

EVEN AS GOPAL'S WIFE CLOSED THE FRONT DOOR, THE DACOITS BROKE IN THROUGH THE BACK DOOR.

COME ON, WOMAN! OUT WITH YOUR GOLD IF YOU VALUE YOUR LIFE!

BUT...BUT... IT'S ALL LOCKED UP.

WHERE ARE THE KEYS?

WITH... WITH THE... MASTER!

DO YOU TAKE US FOR FOOLS? GIVE US THE KEYS! YOUR WIFE SAID...

MY WIFE? I'VE NEVER SEEN THE WOMAN BEFORE!

WHAT! DENYING YOUR OWN WIFE! YOU COWARD! WE'LL TEACH YOU TO TELL LIES!

JUST THEN, GOPAL CAME BACK WITH THE ROYAL SOLDIERS.

IT WORKED! MY PLAN WORKED! BUT IT'S TIME I RESCUED THAT POOR FOOL!

THE DACOITS WERE TAKEN BY SURPRISE.

WELL! THAT SETTLES THE DACOITS. NOW, WHERE'S THAT THIEF YOU TOLD US ABOUT?

YOU MEAN THE MASTER! LET'S LEAVE HIM ALONE! HE HAS BEEN PUNISHED ENOUGH FOR HIS CRIME.

# GOPAL AND GOVINDA

GOPAL'S NEIGHBOUR, GOVINDA, WAS ALWAYS DAY-DREAMING AND HIS WIFE KEPT PACE WITH HIM.

I'VE BEEN THINKING. AS SOON AS I GET SOME MONEY, I SHALL BUY A COW.

THEN WE'RE SOON GOING TO NEED EXTRA POTS. I'D BETTER GO OUT AND BUY SOME.

SO GOVINDA'S WIFE WENT MARKETING. WHEN SHE RETURNED—

WHAT'S ALL THIS?

POTS FOR THE MILK, BUTTER, BUTTERMILK AND GHEE THAT WE'LL GET FROM OUR COW.

OH GOOD! BUT WE NEED ONLY FOUR. WHAT'S THE FIFTH ONE FOR?

OH, THAT! THAT'S FOR CARRYING A LITTLE MILK TO MY SISTER!

CARRYING MILK TO YOUR SISTER?

WITHOUT MY PERMISSION? HOW DARE YOU!

IF I CAN MILK THE COW AND LOOK AFTER IT, I'LL DO WHAT I LIKE WITH ITS MILK!

YOU WON'T! IT'S MY COW. I'VE PAID FOR IT, YOU...

...IMPUDENT WOMAN! AWAY WITH YOU AND YOUR USELESS POTS!

GOPAL RUSHED INTO GOVINDA'S HOUSE.

NOW! NOW! STOP IT!

WHAT ON EARTH IS THE MATTER?

THIS WOMAN IS GOING TO GIVE OUR COW'S MILK AWAY TO HER SISTER!

YOUR COW? WHICH COW?

THE COW I'M GOING TO BUY WHEN I HAVE THE MONEY.

OH! I SEE. BUT YOU DON'T HAVE A COW YET!

# GOPAL AND THE HILSA-FISH

IT WAS THE SEASON FOR HILSA-FISH. FISHERMEN COULD THINK OF NOTHING BUT HILSA-FISH.

FISHMONGERS SOLD NOTHING BUT HILSA-FISH.

COME, BUY. THE PRICE OF HILSA IS DOWN TODAY.

HOUSEHOLDERS COULD TALK OF NOTHING BUT HILSA-FISH.

HOW MUCH DID YOU PAY FOR THAT HILSA?

YOU WOULDN'T BELIEVE IT IF I TOLD YOU.

AND IN THE PALACE TOO THE COURTIERS COULD DISCUSS NOTHING BUT HILSA-FISH.

YOUR MAJESTY, YOU SHOULD HAVE SEEN THE HUGE HILSA I CAUGHT. IT WAS...

STOP IT!

ARE YOU A COURTIER OR A FISHERMAN?

THE COURTIER FELL SILENT WITH DOWNCAST EYES. THE KING FELT GUILTY.

I'M SORRY I LOST MY TEMPER. IT IS THE SEASON FOR HILSA-FISH AND NO ONE...

...NOT EVEN GOPAL CAN STOP ANYONE FROM TALKING ABOUT HILSA-FISH. NOT EVEN FOR FIVE MINUTES!

OH, I THINK I COULD, YOUR MAJESTY.

THEN LET ME SEE YOU BUY A HUGE HILSA AND BRING IT TO THE PALACE WITHOUT ANYONE ASKING YOU A WORD ABOUT IT!

I ACCEPT THE CHALLENGE, YOUR MAJESTY.

A FEW DAYS LATER—

WHY IS YOUR FACE HALF-SHAVEN?

I'M DRESSING UP TO BUY A FISH.

WHAT'S THE MATTER WITH YOU? WHY ARE YOU SMEARING YOURSELF WITH ASH?

I TOLD YOU— I'M DRESSING UP TO BUY A HILSA-FISH.

LISTEN TO ME! PLEASE. YOU CAN'T POSSIBLY GO OUT IN THOSE DISGRACEFUL RAGS! WHAT ARE YOU UP TO?

HOW MANY TIMES MUST I TELL YOU, WOMAN? I AM OUT TO BUY A HUGE HILSA-FISH.

IT'S HAPPENED TO HIM! HE'S GONE MAD!

GOPAL BOUGHT THE HILSA-FISH AND STARTED WALKING TOWARDS THE PALACE.

MOTHER, LOOK AT THAT MAN! ISN'T HE COMICAL?

HE MUST BE A MADMAN.

HUSH! I THINK HE'S A MYSTIC.

WHEN GOPAL REACHED THE COURT—

WHAT DO YOU WANT?

I WANT TO SEE THE KING!

YOU CAN'T SEE THE KING! GET AWAY WITH YOU!

GOPAL BEGAN TO DANCE AND SING LOUDLY.

INSIDE THE PALACE—

THE MAN IS CRAZY!

THROW HIM OUT AT ONCE!

I WANT TO SEE THE KING. LET ME IN!

BRING THAT MAN TO ME AT ONCE!

YES, YOUR MAJESTY.

GOPAL WAS BROUGHT BEFORE THE KING.

IT'S GOPAL!

THE MAN HAS LOST HIS MIND!

I THINK IT'S ONE OF HIS CRAZY JOKES.

ALL RIGHT, GOPAL. OUT WITH IT! WHY ARE YOU DRESSED UP IN THIS RIDICULOUS FASHION?

YOUR MAJESTY, YOU SEEM TO HAVE FORGOTTEN SOMETHING!

FORGOTTEN SOMETHING?

STRANGELY ENOUGH NO ONE SEEMS TO BE INTERESTED IN HILSA-FISH TODAY! FROM THE MARKET TO THE PALACE AND IN THE COURT, NOT A SOUL HAS SPOKEN A WORD ABOUT HILSA-FISH!

ONLY THEN DID THE KING REMEMBER THE CHALLENGE HE HAD DOWN TO GOPAL.

HA! HA! WELL GOPAL, CONGRATULATIONS! YOU HAVE ACHIEVED THE IMPOSSIBLE ONCE AGAIN!

# GOPAL COUNTS THE STARS

YOU HAVEN'T BEEN LISTENING, YOUR MAJESTY. AND THAT WAS ONE OF MY BEST JOKES!

WILL YOU LEAVE ME ALONE! I AM IN NO MOOD FOR YOUR JOKES.

I SEE, THEN IT MUST BE THE NAWAB AGAIN. WHAT IS IT THIS TIME?

OH, NOTHING MUCH, HE ONLY WANTS A CENSUS OF ALL THE STARS IN THE SKY! WHAT DOES HE THINK I AM? A MAGICIAN?

LEAVE IT TO ME, YOUR MAJESTY? IF I COULD MEASURE THE EARTH, I CAN COUNT THE STARS, TOO! ALL I NEED IS A FLOCK OF SHEEP.

A FLOCK OF SHEEP? WHAT HAVE SHEEP TO DO WITH STARS?

YOU'LL FIND OUT, BY AND BY, YOUR MAJESTY.

GOPAL TOOK THE SHEEP TO MURSHIDABAD AND WAITED OUTSIDE THE MOSQUE.

AH! HERE COMES THE NAWAB FOR HIS MORNING PRAYERS.

TWO THOUSAND ONE HUNDRED AND FIFTY-FOUR. TWO THOUSAND ONE HUNDRED AND FIFTY-FIVE...

WHAT'S THAT FELLOW UP TO?

...TWO THOUSAND ONE HUNDRED AND FIFTY-SIX. TWO THOUSAND ONE HUNDRED AND...

HEY, YOU!